FINGERS CROSSED

Thirteen stories and thirteen poems for nine-year-olds

Hello! The first thing I should tell you is that I'm not nine years old myself—but I've done my best to pick the right poems and stories for this book by sharing them with people who are. Of course, you don't have to be nine years old to enjoy them. You may be quite a bit younger or much, much older and still find there's plenty here to catch your fancy. Also you don't have to read the book in any particular order. Feel free to dodge about or even start at the back and finish at the front if this is what you prefer. One of the nice things about an anthology is that every reader can tackle it in a personal way.

When I finished this collection I discovered I'd come up with exactly thirteen poems and exactly thirteen stories. This was just a fluke but it bothered me for a while because I couldn't help remembering the old saying about thirteen being 'unlucky for some'. In the end I decided to trust my own luck and hope the opposite can also be true . . . which is why I've called the anthology FINGERS CROSSED.

Chris Powling

To
Jasmine

happy birthday
from tiahna

6th May 1985

FINGERS CROSSED

*Thirteen stories and thirteen poems
for nine-year-olds*

Chris Powling

Illustrated by Jean Baylis

Blackie

For Kate
looking back six years

British Library Cataloguing in Publication Data
Powling, Chris
Fingers crossed.
I. Title   II. Baylis, Jean
828'.91409   PZ7

ISBN 0-216-92113-9

Blackie and Son Ltd
7 Leicester Place
London WC2H 7BP

Printed in Great Britain by
Thomson Litho Ltd, East Kilbride, Scotland

Contents

Spooky

Different things frighten different people but most of us get jittery about *something*. Often it's something completely imaginary such as the Night Bird in Ursula Wolfel's story or the Invisible Beast in Jack Prelutsky's poem or the mysterious figures with swords described by Michael McHugh. At least, I think these creatures are imaginary . . .

Anyway, we can be quite certain John Ruskin invented his wonderful character The South West Wind Esquire, who appears in his tale 'The King of the Golden River' . . . or can we? Maybe deep inside every spooky story there's a tiny truth trying to get out—like the kids who long to escape from Mordecai Richler's Children's Prison. This comes from his story 'Jacob Two-Two Meets the Hooded Fang' which makes me laugh out loud every time I read it.

The Night Bird

URSULA WOLFEL

There once was a boy who was always very frightened whenever he had to stay in the flat alone at night. His parents often went out in the evening, and then the boy was so frightened that he couldn't get to sleep.

He could hear something rustling: it was as if there was someone in the room, breathing.

He heard a creak and a groan: it sounded as if there was something moving about under his bed.

But the worst thing of all was the Night Bird.

The boy could always see it sitting out there on the window-sill. It never moved except when a car went past down below, and then it would flap its wings and the boy could see the huge shadow they made on the ceiling of his room.

The boy told his parents about being afraid. But all they said was: 'Don't be a baby! You're just imagining it all.' And they still went on going out in the evening. They couldn't see the Bird and they didn't take the story seriously.

Then once when the boy was alone again the
doorbell rang.

The boy went rigid with fear.

It rang again.

It rang and rang.

And then it stopped and for a long time
everything was quiet.

Then something began to scratch at the wall of the house. The Night Bird! Now it was climbing up the wall with its long claws. Now it had reached the window-sill. And now it was banging on the window with its beak! Once, twice, over and over again, louder and louder—and soon the glass would break and the Bird would come leaping into the room!

The boy grabbed the flower vase from the table near his bed and hurled it at the window.

The glass shattered. There was a rush of wind into the room so that the curtain blew high up against the wall. And the Bird was gone.

In the street below the boy heard his mother and father calling.

He raced into the hall and in the dark found the light switch straight away, and the button that opened the downstairs door. Then he tore open the door of the flat and ran to meet his parents.

He laughed out loud, he was so glad that they were there. But they began to scold him. Their smart evening clothes were soaked with water from the flower vase.

'What on earth is going on?' demanded his father. 'Now the window's broken!'

'And just look at my coat!' cried his mother.

'The Night Bird was at the window,' said the boy. 'The Night Bird was pecking at the window with his beak.'

'Rubbish!' said his father. 'We'd forgotten our key and you didn't hear the bell. That's why we banged on your window with a pole from the building site.'

'But it was the Night Bird, really!' said the boy. 'It was the Night Bird!'

But his parents didn't understand. They still went on going out in the evening, leaving the boy alone.

He was still afraid and he still heard the rustling and the creaking and the groaning. But that was not so bad.

Because the Night Bird never came back. He had driven it away. He had driven it away all by himself.

The Invisible Beast

JACK PRELUTSKY

The beast that is invisible
is stalking through the park,
but you cannot see it coming
though it isn't very dark.
Oh you know it's out there somewhere
though just why you cannot tell,
but although you cannot see it
it can see you very well.

You sense its frightful features
and its great ungainly form,
and you wish that you were home now
where it's cosy, safe and warm.
And you know it's coming closer
for you smell its awful smell,
and although you cannot see it
it can see you very well.

Oh your heart is beating faster,
beating louder than a drum,
for you hear its footsteps falling
and your body's frozen numb.
And you cannot scream for terror
and your fear you cannot quell,
for although you cannot see it
it can see you very well.

Gluck's Strange Visitor

JOHN RUSKIN

It was drawing towards winter, and very cold
weather, when one day the two elder brothers
had gone out, with their usual warning to little
Gluck, who was left to mind the roast, that he
was to let nobody in, and give nothing out.
Gluck sat down quite close to the fire, for it

was raining very hard, and the kitchen walls were by no means dry or comfortable-looking. He turned and turned, and the roast got nice and brown.

'What a pity,' thought Gluck, 'my brothers never ask anybody to dinner. I'm sure, when they've got such a nice piece of mutton as this, and nobody else has got so much as a piece of dry bread, it would do their hearts good to have somebody to eat it with them.'

Just as he spoke, there came a double knock at the house door, yet heavy and dull, as though the knocker had been tied up—more like a puff than a knock.

'It must be the wind,' said Gluck; 'nobody else would venture to knock double knocks at our door.' He went to the window, opened it, and put his head out to see who it was.

It was the most extraordinary-looking little gentleman that he had ever seen in his life. He had a very large nose, slightly brass-coloured; his cheeks were very round, and very red, and looked like he'd been blowing a fire for the last eight-and-forty hours; his eyes twinkled merrily through long silky eyelashes, his moustaches curled twice round like a corkscrew on each side of his mouth, and his hair, of a curious mixed pepper-and-salt colour, descended far over his shoulders. He was about four feet six in height, and wore a conical-pointed cap of nearly the same altitude, decorated with a black feather some three feet long. His coat was covered up by the swelling folds of an enormous black, glossy-looking cloak, which must have been very much too long in calm weather, as the wind, whistling round the old house, carried it clear out from the wearer's shoulders to about four times his own length.

Gluck was so perfectly paralysed by the appearance of his visitor, that he remained fixed without uttering a word, until the old gentleman, having performed another, and a more energetic concerto on the knocker, turned round to look after his fly-away cloak. In so doing he caught sight of Gluck's little yellow head jammed in the window, with his mouth and eyes very wide open indeed.

'Hallo!' said the little gentleman, 'that's not the way to answer the door; I'm wet; let me in.'

To do the little gentleman justice, he *was* wet. His feather hung down between his legs like a beaten puppy's tail, dripping like an umbrella; and from the ends of his moustaches the water was running into his waistcoat pockets, and out again like a mill stream.

'I beg pardon, sir,' said Gluck. 'I'm very sorry, but I really can't.'

'Can't what?' said the old gentleman.

'I can't let you in, sir—I can't indeed; my

brothers would beat me to death, sir, if I thought of such a thing. What do you want, sir?'

'Want?' said the old gentleman. 'I want fire and shelter; and there's your great fire there blazing, crackling, and dancing on the wall, with nobody to feel it. Let me in, I say; I only want to warm myself. Never mind your brothers. I'll talk to them.'

'Pray, sir, don't do any such thing.' said Gluck. 'I can't let you stay till they come; they'd be the death of me.'

'Dear me,' said the old gentleman, 'I'm very sorry to hear that. How long may I stay?'

'Only till the mutton's done, sir,' replied Gluck, 'and it's very brown.' Then the old gentleman walked into the kitchen and sat himself down on the hob, with the top of his cap poked up the chimney, for it was a great deal too high for the roof.

'You'll soon dry there, sir,' said Gluck, and sat down again to turn the mutton. But the old gentleman did *not* dry there, but went on drip, drip, dripping among the cinders, and the fire fizzed, and sputtered, and began to look very black and uncomfortable; never was such a cloak; every fold in it ran like a gutter.

'I beg pardon, sir,' said Gluck at length, after watching the water spreading in long, quick-silver streams over the floor for a quarter of

an hour; 'mayn't I take your cloak?'

'No, thank you,' said the old gentleman.

'Your cap, sir.'

'I am all right, thank you,' said the old gentleman rather gruffly.

'But—sir—I'm very sorry,' said Gluck, hesitatingly; 'but you're putting the fire out.'

'It'll take longer to do the mutton then,' replied his visitor dryly.

Gluck was very much puzzled by the behaviour of his guest; it was such a strange mixture of coolness and humility. He turned away at the string thoughtfully for another five minutes.

'That mutton looks very nice,' said the old gentleman at length. 'Can't you give me a little bit!'

'Impossible, sir,' said Gluck.

'I'm very hungry,' continued the old gentleman; 'I've had nothing to eat yesterday, nor to-day. They surely couldn't miss a bit from the knuckle!'

He spoke in so very melancholy a tone, that it quite melted Gluck's heart.

'They promised me one slice to-day, sir,' said he; 'I can give you that, but not a bit more.'

'That's a good boy,' said the old gentleman again.

Then Gluck warmed a plate, and sharpened a knife. 'I don't care if I do get beaten for it,' thought he. Just as he had cut a large slice out of the mutton, there came a tremendous rap at the door. The old gentleman jumped off the hob, as if it had suddenly become inconveniently warm. Gluck fitted the slice into the mutton again, with desperate efforts to get it back in the right place, and ran to open the door.

'What did you keep us waiting in the rain for?' said Schwartz, as he walked in, throwing his umbrella in Gluck's face. 'Ay! what for, indeed, you little vagabond?' said Hans, administering an educational box on the ear, as he followed his brother into the kitchen.

'Bless my soul!' said Schwartz when he opened the door.

'Amen!' said the little gentleman, who had taken his cap off, and was standing in the middle of the kitchen, bowing with the utmost possible speed.

'Who's that?' said Schwartz, catching up a rolling-pin, and turning to Gluck with a frown.

'I don't know, indeed, brother,' said Gluck in great terror.

'How did he get in?' roared Schwartz.

'My dear brother,' Gluck pleaded. 'He was so *very* wet!'

The rolling-pin was descending on Gluck's head; but, at the instant, the old gentleman stuck out his pointed cap, on which it crashed with a shock that shook the water out of it all over the room. What was very odd, the rolling-pin no sooner touched the cap, then it flew out of Schwartz's hand, spinning like a straw in a high wind, and fell into the corner at the farther end of the room.

'Who are you, sir?' demanded Schwartz, turning upon him.

'What's your business?' snarled Hans.

'I'm a poor old man, sir,' the little gentleman began very modestly, 'and I saw your fire through the window; and begged shelter for a quarter of an hour.'

'Have the goodness to walk out again, then,' said Schwartz. 'We've quite enough water in our kitchen, without making it into a drying house.'

'It is a cold day to turn an old man out, sir; look at my grey hairs.' They hung down to his shoulders, as I told you before.

'Ay!' said Hans, 'there are enough of them to keep you warm. Walk!'

'I'm very, very hungry, sir; couldn't you spare me a bit of bread before I go?'

'Bread, indeed,' said Schwartz; 'do you suppose we've nothing to do with our bread but to give to such red-nosed fellows as you?'

'Why don't you sell your feather?' said Hans, sneeringly. 'Out with you!'

'A little bit,' said the old gentleman.

'Be off!' said Schwartz.

'Pray, gentlemen.'

'Off, and be hanged!' cried Hans, seizing him by the collar. But he had no sooner touched the old gentleman's collar, then away he went after the rolling-pin, spinning round and round, till he fell into the corner on top of it. Then Schwartz was very angry, and ran at the old gentleman to turn him out; but he also had hardly touched him, when away he went after Hans and the rolling-pin, and hit his head against the wall as he tumbled into the corner. And so there they lay, all three.

Then the old gentleman spun himself round with velocity in the opposite direction; continued to spin until his long cloak was all wound neatly about him; clapped his cap on his head, very much on one side (for it could not stand upright without going through the ceiling), gave an additional twist to his corkscrew moustaches, and replied with perfect coolness: 'Gentlemen, I wish you a very good morning. At twelve o'clock to-night, I'll call again; after such a refusal of hospitality as I have just experienced, you will not be surprised if that visit is the last I ever pay you . . .'

Such a night it was! Howling wind, and rushing rain, without intermission. The brothers had just sense enough left to put up all the shutters, and double bar the door, before they went to bed. They usually slept in the same room. As the clock struck twelve, they were both awakened by a tremendous crash. Their door burst open with a violence that shook the house from top to bottom.

'What's that?' cried Schwartz.

'Only I,' said the little gentleman.

The two brothers sat up on their bolster, and stared into the darkness. The room was full of water, and by a misty moonbeam, which found its way through a hole in the shutter, they could see, in the midst of it, an enormous foam globe, spinning round, and bobbing up and down like a cork, on which, as on a most luxurious cushion, reclined the little old gentleman, cap and all. There was plenty of room for it now, for the roof was off.

'Sorry to inconvenience you,' said their visitor, ironically. 'I'm afraid your beds are dampish; perhaps you had better go to your brother's room; I've left the ceiling on there.'

They required no second warning, but rushed into Gluck's room, wet through, and in an agony of terror.

'You'll find my card on the kitchen table,' the old gentleman called after them. 'Remember the *last* visit.'

'Pray Heaven it may!' said Schwartz, shuddering. And the foam globe disappeared.

Dawn came at last, and the two brothers looked out of Gluck's little window in the morning. The Treasure Valley was one mass of ruin and desolation. The flood had swept away trees, crops, and cattle, and left, in their stead, a waste of red sand and grey mud. The two brothers crept, shivering and horror-struck into the kitchen. The water had gutted the whole first-floor; corn, money, almost every movable thing had been swept away, and there was left only a small white card on the kitchen table. On it, in large, breezy, long-legged letters were engraved the words:

~South West Wind~
Esquire

Journey's End

MICHAEL MCHUGH

Through the windscreen, up the hill,
the figures catch the eye,
motionless, in silhouette
against the evening sky.

Driving up the rising road
we stare at them in dread:
miniature, then looming large,
they frame the way ahead.

Just as we're abreast of them
the engine coughs and fades.
We roll in silence to a halt—
to face a line of blades.

The blades glint in the furnace-glow
of the molten sun,
their handles fast in shadowed fists
taunting us to run.

They close in to encircle us;
we huddle up in fright.
They peer in at the windows,
blotting out the light.

Shrouded in this inner dark
we mouth unuttered screams;
a grimmer vision couldn't haunt
the grimmest of our dreams.

We scuffle to secure the locks
but numbness dulls each hand,
seeping into every limb,
as if it's filled with sand.

Still as stone, we contemplate
the leaving of our lives
as first one ear, then all, pick up
the sharpening of knives.

Jacob Two-Two Meets The Hooded Fang

MORDECAI RICHLER

Jacob Two-Two's guards on his seemingly endless journey were called Master Fish and Mistress Fowl.

'I suppose,' snarled Master Fish, 'that your daddy loves you?'

'Oh, yes,' replied Jacob Two-Two. 'Oh yes.'

'Well, I don't, you little stinker. In fact, I think you're perfectly horrible.'

Jacob Two-Two lowered his head.

'I can see,' sneered Mistress Fowl, 'that you're used to being treated kindly. Well, I'll bet your mother reads you a story before tucking you in at night.'

Jacob Two-Two smiled in fond remembrance. He nodded twice.

'Well, you repulsive little brat, you just wait until you hear the bedtime stories we read over the loudspeaker system in the children's prison.'

Jacob Two-Two loved stories. 'Are they good ones?' he asked hopefully. 'Are they good ones?'

'They certainly are,' said Master Fish, 'if you

like to tremble in the dark and listen to tales of red-eyed witches.'

'Or bloodthirsty vampires,' said Mistress Fowl.

'Or Kidnappers.'

'Or Monsters from outer space.'

Jacob Two-Two shuddered.

'The children's prison,' said Master Fish, delighted, 'awaits your pleasure.'

'But why?' asked Jacob Two-Two, 'why a prison for children?'

Master Fish was outraged. Mistress Fowl was appalled.

'Don't you think there ought to be a place,' snarled Master Fish, 'for little people so utterly hopeless they can't even ride a two-wheel bicycle?'

'Or dial a telephone number,' sneered Mistress Fowl.

"Or count the laundry?'

"Or even cross the street by themselves?'

Jacob Two-Two swallowed his tears.

'Look here, you useless twerp, little people are always doing the wrong thing.'

'Like waking up their parents at six o'clock on a Sunday morning to say the sun is out.'

'Or gobbling all the peaches on the kitchen table before their elder brothers and sisters come down.'

Or, Jacob Two-Two had to admit to himself, recalling the incident with a shudder, running to answer the telephone and telling Daniel's girl friend that his brother couldn't take the call, because he was on the toilet doing his dump.

'Admit it, clunkhead,' snapped Master Fish, 'how many times have you watered all the house plants only an hour after your mother had done it?'

'I was only trying to be helpful,' protested Jacob Two-Two. 'I was only trying to be helpful.'

'Yes, certainly. But you drowned them, didn't you?'

'Ignorant little troublemaker!'

Jacob Two-Two retreated, convinced by his tormentors that there simply had to be a prison for little people as obnoxious as he was, but in his worst dreams he was not prepared for what lay ahead.

Fog, fog everywhere.

Mistress Fowl smiled. Master Fish began to whistle a happy tune. And for the very first time, they actually removed their dark glasses.

Jacob Two-Two shivered. It was so cold. As his eyes adjusted to the dim light, the first thing he made out, in the distance, were two gigantic chimney stacks, filthy gray fog billowing from both of them.

'Look,' said Mistress Fowl, 'We're almost there.'

As they emerged from a field of tall spiky grass onto a muddy shore, Jacob Two-Two made out a sign that read:

THIS WAY TO SLIMERS' ISLE
FROM WHICH NO BRATS
RETURN

The sign pointed toward a rowing boat, a leaky rowing boat, and Jacob Two-Two was flung into it by his guards.

'I'll row,' said Master Fish.

'I'll steer,' said Mistress Fowl.

'And you, my dear,' they shouted together, 'will bail. *Or we might sink,*' they added, bursting into laughter.

Rusty can in hand, Jacob Two-Two bailed furiously, for the murky waters, he quickly saw, were infested with blood thirsty sharks and slimy crocodiles, their jaws snapping hungrily. And it was no better once they reached the opposite shore, where the first thing to greet Jacob Two-Two was a slithering snake.

'Poisonous, of course,' said Master Fish.

The children's prison, Jacob Two-Two learned, was built on a marshy island in the foggiest part of England, a place where the sun never shone. The only birds that ever flew over the island were buzzards, and the land could

support no animal life other than grey wolverines with yellow snaggle-teeth and millions of deathwatch beetles. There were no flowers, boasted Master Fish, but nettles thrived everywhere, hiding the quicksand, added Mistress Fowl.

The prison itself, Jacob Two-Two saw, was built of clammy grey stone. As he approached, its ugly towers, choked with vines that yielded poisonous blackberries, rose gloomily into the never-ending fog.

'Home, sweet home,' cried Mistress Fowl.

An enormous flashing sign proclaimed:

TREMBLE, KIDS!
SHIVER!
SHUDDER!
YOU ARE APPROACHING
THE LAIR
OF THE
HOODED FANG!

Underneath, neon blood dripped into a see-thing, steaming cauldron, and a perpetual laughing machine cackled '*Ho! Ho! Ho!*'

Once inside the prison, Master Fish and Mistress Fowl thrust Jacob Two-Two into the warden's lair. The warden was known as The Hooded Fang. Jacob Two-Two, looking very pale, discovered him sprawled on the floor, smelly and unshaven, sharpening his fangs by gnawing on a beef bone, a marrow bone. The Hooded Fang seized Jacob Two-Two's charge sheet, muttering to himself as he clutched it between his paws. 'Mmmnnn,' said The Hooded Fang, 'insulting behaviour to a big person, eh? We'll soon cure that, we will. Remove this desperado to the lowest, dampest dungeon and put him on a diet of stale bread and water. My shaving water! Ho, ho, ho!'

'Can I have two slices, please?' asked Jacob Two-Two. 'Can I have two slices?'

'You see,' said The Hooded Fang, strutting, 'he's only been here two minutes and he's begging for mercy. Am I tough! Oh, boy, I'm the toughest!' The Hooded Fang growled at Jacob Two-Two. He bared his fangs. 'Shall I tell you why I hate kids more than anything in this world?'

'Please do,' said Jacob Two-Two. 'Please do.'

The Hooded Fang dismissed Master Fish and Mistress Fowl and locked the door to his lair.

'Once,' he began, 'I was a star, with my own dressing room. The Hooded Fang, most hated and vile villain in all of wrestling. Why, as I made my way from my dressing room into the arena, the boos were sufficient to raise the roof beams. And the minute I stepped into the ring, the fans pelted me with stinking fish, rotten eggs, and overripe tomatoes. Oh, it was lovely! Then,' said The Hooded Fang, his eyes suddenly charged with menace, 'it happened. One dreadful evening in Doncaster, just as I slipped between the ropes, waiting for the eggs and fish to fly . . . *a child laughed*. A child, standing on a chair in the front row, pointed at me; laughed out loud, and said, "He's not terrible, Daddy, he's funny!" *Funny*? Desperately, I rolled my eyes. I bared my fangs. I made menacing faces. But nobody threw anything. Not one little rotten egg. The child wouldn't stop laughing. And, before you knew it, the whole arena was convulsed. The more I growled, the louder they laughed. When my opponent entered the ring, I immediately poked my thumb into his eye, but instead of hitting back, he just fell against the ropes, roaring with laughter.'

The Hooded Fang blew his nose. His head hung heavy.

'These things get around, you know. It was in the newspapers. Soon, wherever I went, all I had to do was crawl through the ropes, and the fans were laughing so hard, tears came to their eyes. *All because a child laughed.* A funny villain is no good, don't you see? No good at all.'

'Oh, I'm sorry, Mr Hooded Fang,' said Jacob Two-Two. 'I'm sorry.'

'Are you?' asked The Hooded Fang, surprised. 'Why?'

'Because you seem to be such a nice man.'

'What?' roared The Hooded Fang. 'How dare you! I'm not nice. I'm horrible, disgusting, mean, vicious, evil, and vile! Now get out of my sight, before I sink my fangs into you. Oh, how I hate kids!'

Words

Words can be tricky—as Charlie found out in this extract from Sheila Lavelle's 'My Best Fiend'. Charlie has a terrible time when she comes across a word with two meanings, one polite and one rude. The trouble is that once we use them words take on a life of their own. Emily Dickinson's poem 'A Word' reminds us about this and so does 'The Word Party' by Richard Edwards. Maybe we should all take a trip to the weird market place invented by Norton Juster where all sorts of language is for sale, and all sorts of strange characters are buying and selling it, including the Humbug and the Spelling Bee whose quarrel ends up burying them both beneath a sort of alphabet avalanche. This passage is taken from 'The Phantom Tollbooth', which is a long, lovely, jokey book about numbers as well as words.

Charlie's Swear Word

SHEILA LAVELLE

Fridays are special days at our school because instead of having Junior Prayers separately like we usually do, the whole school has Assembly together in the big hall and Miss Collingwood takes us. Miss Collingwood is the headmistress and I think she's lovely. She's tall and dark-haired and pretty and she's got a nice gentle voice and a kind smile. Nobody has ever seen her get mad or heard her shout and somehow she never seems to need to, because everybody always does what she wants anyway. And she never orders people about, she always asks them nicely. Not like my bossy Miss Bennett.

I like going to Assembly with the Upper School. The teachers sit on a row of chairs on the platform, and it's just like a stage and you can have a good look at them all. We have to stand in front of them and stare straight at their legs and feet, and you can't help noticing if the lady teachers have got holes in their tights and what colour socks the men teachers are wearing and whether they have polished their shoes.

First of all we have to sing a hymn together and Angela and I like to watch to see which

33

teachers are really singing properly and which ones are just yawning or looking out of the window. And Mr Young, the music teacher, thumps away like anything on the piano and plays a lot of twiddly bits between the verses and Angela thinks he's even better than Elton John. Then we say our prayers and one of the big boys or girls from the top class reads the Lesson only I don't know why it's called the Lesson because it's just a bit out of the Bible and you don't really learn anything much. And sometimes it's Roger Grant's turn to read the Lesson, and then all the girls stare at him because he's the head boy and he's thirteen and he's got shiny brown hair and white teeth and looks exactly like Donny Osmond and everybody wants to marry him except Angela who has made up her mind to marry a king.

After the Lesson we all sing another hymn and then Miss Collingwood gives us one of her little chats. She calls it a chat but it's not really because she's the only one who's allowed to talk and we all have to stand still and not fidget. Miss Collingwood's little chats are about all sorts of things, like Cleanliness, and Truthfulness, and Helping Others, and stuff like that, and somehow she always makes you end up feeling ashamed of yourself for not being as clean or as honest or as helpful as you should be, and you secretly make up your mind to try harder in the future.

One Friday morning Miss Collingwood's little chat was about Bad Language. Some boys at the back of the hall started to snigger when she said that, but they soon stopped when she gave them one of her looks. She told us that one of the Upper School boys, who really ought to know better, had been heard saying a very rude word on a bus. Miss Collingwood didn't tell us what the rude word was which was a shame because I was dying to know. But it must have been something very bad indeed because a lady on the bus was so shocked that she told the conductor, and the conductor took the boy's name and reported him to the school.

Miss Collingwood was very upset. She said it was a terrible thing for young people to swear and it damaged the school's good reputation and what a pity it was that so many of us were getting into this bad habit. She was determined not to let it happen in her school. She gazed down at us earnestly and we all turned our faces up towards her like rows of flowers looking at the sun. You felt as if she could see inside you and read what you were thinking and it was a very uncomfortable feeling.

'I'm going to ask you all to help me,' she said. 'Because there's only one way to stamp this out before it spreads. Now, you all know how much I dislike people telling tales, but I feel that in this important matter your loyalty to the school, and to me, should come before your loyalty to your friends. So, if any of you hear any person in this school using bad language I want you to tell one of the teachers at once, and the teacher will send that person to me. I know it's unpleasant, but I believe that in this case it's necessary. I'm sure I can rely on your support.'

Miss Collingwood gave us one of her nicest smiles and then nodded at Mr Young who was still sitting at the piano. He began to play his favourite marching tune and I think it's called Spaghetti March or something like that, and we all filed out with a lot of whispering and giggling and everybody wondering who would be the first to get reported and feeling sure it wouldn't be them.

When we got back to the classroom it was time for our History lesson. I usually like History lessons, but this particular morning I couldn't seem to concentrate very well because I had a letter from my Uncle Barrie in my satchel. It arrived just as I was leaving the house and I hadn't had time to open it yet. Uncle Barrie writes to me a lot and I love getting his letters because they're long and chatty and he puts funny poems in and sometimes there's even a postal order. So I kept thinking about it and I didn't take much notice of the History lesson at all.

The lesson was about Captain Cook's voyages and the old-fashioned sailing ships and how the sailors kept on dying of a horrible disease called scurvy. And it was all because nobody had discovered that the disease could be prevented as easily as anything by eating fresh fruit and green vegetables that have something called Vitamin C in them. And then this Captain Cook found out that if he made all his sailors eat lemons and limes then nobody on his ship got scurvy and the Navy were so pleased that they gave him a medal. At the end of the lesson Miss Bennett started to ask us some questions about it and it was just my rotten luck that she picked on me first.

'Charlotte,' she said. 'Will you please tell us what happens to people who don't eat green vegetables.'

And without thinking I stood up and said the first thing that came into my head.

'They don't get any pudding,' I said, and gazed round the room in surprise as everybody burst out laughing. That fat Laurence Parker almost choked and even Miss Bennett's mouth twitched in a funny way and I thought she was going to laugh, too. She didn't though. She got cross instead.

'Charlotte Ellis!' she snapped. 'You haven't listened to a single word this lesson. You will stay indoors at break time and read the chapter on Captain Cook in your history book.'

'Yes, Miss Bennett,' I said, and tried to look sorry. But I didn't mind a bit really, because it would give me a chance to read my letter from Uncle Barrie in peace.

So when the bell went at playtime and everybody else went out into the playground with their apples and biscuits and Miss Bennett went off to the staffroom to have her coffee, I stayed in the classroom all by myself and read about Captain Cook. And it was very interesting, much more interesting than when Miss Bennett told it. She's the sort of person who could make even Doctor Who sound boring.

When I'd read the whole chapter I opened my letter from Uncle Barrie and it was lovely, all about the wild kids in his school in London and about the plays and films he had been to see, and there was a postal order for fifty pence and a funny poem that made me giggle.

'There was a young sailor called Plum,
Who drank a whole barrel of rum,
He made himself drunk
And fell off his bunk
And landed flat on his elbow.'

I was just putting the letter away in my satchel when Miss Bennett came back into the classroom.

'Well, Charlotte,' she said. 'Have you read all about Captain Cook?'

'Yes, Miss Bennett,' I said meekly.

'And now do you know what happens to people who don't eat green vegetables?'

'Yes, Miss Bennett,' I said. 'They get scurvy.'

'Very well, Charlotte,' said Miss Bennett. 'You may go out for the last five minutes of break time. And please see that you pay more attention in future.'

'Yes, Miss Bennett. Thank you, Miss Bennett,' I said gratefully. Then I ran out of the room and down the corridor before she could change her mind. So that was how I got to the playground just in time to see Angela's accident.

They were all playing 'What's The Time Mr Wolf?' and Laurence Parker was the wolf. It may seem a bit of a silly game to play, but if you have to spend your playtime in a sort of concrete cage with iron railings round it there's not much else you can do except play silly games. Anyway, everybody was marching along behind Laurence Parker shouting 'What's the TIME Mr Wolf?' and he kept saying it was five o'clock or seven o'clock or half-past eleven and then suddenly he shouted 'DINNER TIME!' and everybody screamed and ran away and Laurence Parker started to chase Angela. I don't know why it is that whenever there's a chasing game going on it's always Angela who gets chased but that's what always happens.

So of course Angela shrieked and dashed away across the playground and that's when that awful Delilah Jones deliberately stuck her foot out in front of Angela and sent her crashing forward onto her knees.

Everybody crowded round and I had to elbow my way to the front to see what was happening. Angela was sitting on the ground holding her left leg which had blood pouring from a great gash in the knee. I noticed that she was keeping her leg sideways so that the blood dripped on the ground because she had her new white lace knee-socks on and she didn't want to get them stained. I knelt beside her and pushed her sock down towards her ankle away from the trickles of blood. She looked a bit pale but apart from that she seemed all right and I sent that nice David Watkins to find the teacher on duty. It's funny that teachers on duty never seem to be around when they're needed and yet they always manage to turn up when you least want them to.

Well, we were all standing around waiting

for the teacher when that fat fool Laurence Parker started pulling Angela's arm and trying to make her stand up. I could see she didn't want to in case she got blood on her sock so I pushed him out of the way.

'Leave her alone, stupid!' I said. 'Can't you see she can't move her bloody leg!'

There was a shocked silence and then everybody started to gasp and say 'Oooh!' Delilah Jones put her hand to her mouth and her eyes went wide.

'Oooh, Charlie Ellis!' she said. 'You SWORE!'

Now what I don't understand is why a perfectly good and useful word like bloody should be a swear word. What else can you call something when it's all covered in blood except bloody? I think it's only a swear word because grown-ups have turned it into one and it's all their fault. And anyway they use it all the time. I even heard my dad say it once when he couldn't find a single pair of socks without holes in them.

'What rubbish!' I said. 'That wasn't swearing. I only said her leg was bloody because it is! Look at it,' I said. 'You can see it's bloody!'

Everybody started talking at once and I could feel my face getting more and more red. 'She said it again!' they said, and 'Ooh, did you hear that!' and 'Ooh, what language!' and they

all pretended to be terribly shocked and before long there was a great crowd around us all having a lovely time saying wasn't Charlie Ellis wicked and not one of them taking the slightest bit of notice of Angela sitting on the ground bleeding to death.

Suddenly everybody went quiet as the teacher on duty arrived and my heart sank because it was Mrs Mason. Mrs Mason is the Scripture teacher and she's horrible. She's always talking about love and forgiveness and she's got a worse temper than anybody I know. I once saw her shaking a poor little kindergarten boy until his teeth nearly fell out because he accidentally put his sticky hands on her skirt.

'Whatever's going on here?' she said, and then she noticed Angela sitting on the ground. 'Oh, my goodness!' she said. 'You have had a nasty tumble.' She knelt at Angela's side and mopped up the worst of the blood with a wad of paper tissues that she had in her pocket. Then she tied a big white handkerchief around Angela's knee. When she'd finished she stood up and looked at us.

'Now,' she said. 'What was all that fuss about?'

Delilah Jones stepped forward. 'Please, Mrs Mason,' she said. 'Charlie Ellis said a bad word.'

Mrs Mason frowned at me. 'Charlie, is this true?' she said.

I shook my head and started to explain but everybody else nodded like mad and said they'd all heard me so what could I do?

'And what was this bad word?' Mrs Mason asked Delilah Jones, but Delilah put her hand over her mouth and went pink and tittered and said she couldn't say it, she just couldn't.

'Well, somebody had better tell me,' said Mrs Mason crossly. 'Miss Collingwood will certainly want to know.' But they all just looked at one another and looked at the ground and nobody said anything because nobody wanted to be the one to say that dreadful word.

'Well, actually, Mrs Mason,' said Delilah Jones at last, and she blushed and stammered like anything. 'Actually, er, Charlie said, er, bloody.'

Mrs Mason looked at Angela. 'Is this true, Angela? I'm sure I can rely on you to tell the truth.'

Angela gazed at Mrs Mason with her eyes all round and innocent, and I knew there was no hope.

'Yes, Mrs Mason,' she said. 'She said it three times.'

I was very upset. 'It's not fair!' I shouted. 'I wasn't swearing at all! I only said that her leg was . . .'

44

'Charlotte!' snapped Mrs Mason. 'That will be quite enough. You'll only make things worse by trying to tell lies about it. You will go straight to Mrs Collingwood's study at once. And you will tell her exactly why I have sent you.'

Everybody watched in silence as I began to trail miserably across the playground to the school. I looked back before I went in and saw that two of the bigger boys had linked hands to make a sort of chair and were carrying Angela back to the classroom. She gave me a wave to show that we were still friends but I didn't wave back. Somehow I just didn't feel like it. I stumped along the corridor to Miss Collingwood's room and knocked on the door so softly you could hardly hear it. Nothing happened so I sat down on the green chair to wait.

The green chair is a wooden seat and it's hard and uncomfortable and painted green and it stays outside Miss Collingwood's room for people who have done bad things to sit on while they wait for Miss Collingwood to see them. And it's awful because you're not allowed to go straight in but you have to knock and then wait until she comes out and sometimes you have to wait ages because she's busy seeing parents and sometimes she's not even there but taking a class somewhere and you might have to sit there for hours. And everybody who walks past knows what you're sitting there for and they shake their heads and go tut-tut and say what a naughty girl you are, and you get more and more ashamed and embarrassed.

But this time I didn't have long to wait. After only a minute or so the door opened and there stood Miss Collingwood, smiling.

'Come in, Charlie,' she said. 'What can I do for you?'

And do you know, I felt so miserable and upset and helpless and sorry for myself that I started to cry. Big tears rolled down my face and I rubbed my eyes and gulped and hiccupped.

'Dear me,' said Miss Collingwood kindly. 'We are in a state.'

I don't know why she said that WE were in a state when it was only me that was in one, but I was glad when she pushed a box of tissues in my hand because crying always gives me a runny nose. She made me sit down in a chair beside her desk and started looking at some papers to give me time to pull myself together.

I blew my nose and mopped up the tears and sniffed a bit. After that I found I was feeling much better. And you won't believe it but when I explained the whole thing to Miss

Collingwood she understood perfectly. She said she felt exactly the same as me about it. She said what a shame it was that people misused the English language and spoiled it for everybody else, and that I hadn't used a bad word at all, it was all a question of context, whatever that means, and I wasn't to worry about it any more. And she patted my hand and gave me one of those posh chocolate peppermint-creams in the little square brown envelopes that people have at dinner parties and promised to explain everything to Mrs Mason. Then she sent me back to the classroom.

When everybody saw my red eyes they thought I must have been in terrible trouble and they were all very nice to me for the rest of that day. I think they were all a bit ashamed of themselves for telling on me because even Laurence Parker gave me one of his toffees.

And of course I was furious with Angela. I even vowed to myself that I would never be friends with her again. But I can never stay cross with her for long, and when it was home time and she hobbled out of school like a wounded hero with a great big sticking plaster on her knee, somehow I couldn't help forgiving her, especially when she wouldn't lean on anybody else's arm but mine.

The Word Party

RICHARD EDWARDS

Loving words clutch crimson roses,
Rude words sniff and pick their noses,
Sly words come dressed up as foxes,
Short words stand on cardboard boxes,
Common words tell jokes and gabble,
Complicated words play Scrabble,
Swear words stamp around and shout,
Hard words stare each other out,
Foreign words look lost and shrug,
Careless words trip on the rug,
Long words slouch with stooping shoulders,

Code words carry secret folders,
Silly words flick rubber bands,
Hyphenated words hold hands,
Strong words show off, bending metal,
Sweet words call each other 'petal',
Small words yawn and suck their thumbs
Till at last the morning comes.
Kind words give our farewell posies . . .

Snap! The dictionary closes.

A Word

EMILY DICKINSON

A word is dead
When it is said,
Some say.

I say it just
Begins to live
That day.

Confusion in the Market Place

NORTON JUSTER

As Milo and Tock, the Watch-dog, approached the market, they could see crowds of people pushing and shouting their way among the stalls, buying and selling, trading and bargaining. Huge wooden-wheeled carts streamed into the market square and long caravans bound for the four corners of the kingdom made ready to leave. Sacks and boxes were piled high waiting to be delivered to the ships that sailed the Sea of Knowledge, and off to one side a group of minstrels sang songs to the delight of those either too young or too old to engage in trade. But above all the noise and tumult of the crowd could be heard the merchants' voices loudly advertising their products.

'Get your fresh-picked ifs, ands, and buts.'

'Hey-yaa, hey-yaa, hey-yaa, nice ripe wheres and whens.'

'Juicy, tempting words for sale.'

So many words and so many people! They were from every place imaginable and some places even beyond that, and they were all busy sorting, choosing, and stuffing things into cases. As soon as one was filled, another was begun. There seemed to be no end to the bustle and activity.

Milo and Tock wandered up and down between the stalls looking at the wonderful assortment of words for sale. There were short ones and easy ones for everyday use, and long and very important ones for special occasions, and even some marvellously fancy ones packed in individual gift boxes for use in royal decrees and pronouncements.

'Step right up, step right up—fancy, best-quality words right here,' announced one man in a booming voice. 'Step right up—ah, what can I do for you, little boy? How about a nice bagful of pronouns—or maybe you'd like our special assortment of names?'

Milo had never thought much about words before, but these looked so good that he longed to have some.

'Look, Tock,' he cried, 'aren't they wonderful?'

'They're fine, if you have something to say,' replied Tock in a tired voice, for he was much more interested in finding a bone than in shopping for new words.

'Maybe if I buy some I can learn how to use them,' said Milo eagerly as he began to pick through the words in the stall. Finally he chose three which looked particularly good to him— "quagmire", "flabbergast", and "upholstery".

He had no idea what they meant, but they looked very grand and elegant.

'How much are these?' he inquired, and when the man whispered the answer he quickly put them back on the shelf and started to walk on.

'Why not take a few pounds of "happys"?' advised the salesman. 'They're much more practical—and very useful for Happy Birthday, Happy New Year, happy days, and happy-go-lucky.'

'I'd like to very much,' began Milo, 'but—'

'Or perhaps you'd be interested in a package of "goods"—always handy for good morning, good afternoon, good evening and good-bye,' he suggested.

Milo did want to buy something, but the only money he had was the coin he needed to get back through the tollbooth, and Tock, of course, had nothing but the time.

'No, thank you,' replied Milo. 'We're just looking.' And they continued on through the market.

As they turned down the last lane of stalls, Milo noticed a wagon that seemed different from the rest. On its side was a small neatly lettered sign that said DO IT YOURSELF, and inside were twenty-six bins filled with all letters of the alphabet from A to Z.

'These are for people who like to make their

own words,' the man in charge informed him. 'You can pick any assortment you like or buy a special box complete with all letters, punctuation marks, and a book of instructions. Here taste an A; they're very good.'

Milo nibbled carefully at the letter and discovered that it was quite sweet and delicious— just the way you'd expect an A to taste.

'I knew you'd like it,' laughed the letter man, popping two G's and an R into his mouth and letting the juice drip down his chin. 'A's are one of our most popular letters. All of them aren't so good,' he confided in a low voice. 'Take the Z, for instance—very dry and saw-dusty. And the X? Why, it tastes like a trunkful of stale air. That's why people hardly ever use them. But most of the others are quite tasty. Try some more.'

He gave Milo an I, which was icy and refreshing, and Tock a crisp, crunchy C.

'Most people are just too lazy to make their own words,' he continued, 'But it's much more fun.'

'Is it difficult? I'm not much good at making words,' admitted Milo, spitting the pips from a P.

'Perhaps I can be of some assistance—a-s-s-i-s-t-a-n-c-e-,' buzzed an unfamiliar voice, and when Milo looked up he saw an enormous bee, at least twice his size, sitting on top of the wagon.

'I am the Spelling Bee,' announced the Spelling Bee. Don't be alarmed—a-l-a-r-m-e-d.'

Tock ducked under the wagon, and Milo, who was not over fond of normal-sized bees began to back away slowly. 'I can spell any-thing—a-n-y-t-h-i-n-g-,' he boasted, testing his wings. 'Try me, try me!'

'Can you spell good-bye?' suggested Milo as he continued to back away.

The bee gently lifted himself into the air and circled lazily over Milo's head.

'Perhaps—p-e-r-h-a-p-s—you are under the misapprehension—m-i-s-a-p-p-r-e-h-e-n-s-i-o-n- that I am dangerous,' he said, turning a smart loop to the left. 'Let me assure—a-s-s-u-r-e- you that my intentions are peaceful—p-e-a-c-e-f-u-l-.' And with that he settled back on top of the wagon and fanned himself with one wing. 'Now,' he panted, 'think of the most difficult word you can and I'll spell it. Hurry up, hurry up!' And he jumped up and down impatiently.

'He looks friendly enough,' thought Milo, not sure just how friendly a friendly bumble-bee should be and tried to think of a very difficult word. 'Spell "vegetable", he suggested, for it was one that always troubled him at school.

'That is a difficult one,' said the bee, winking at the letter man. 'Let me see now. . . .hmmmmmmmm. . . .' He frowned and wiped his brow and paced slowly back and forth on top of the wagon. 'How much time do I have?'

'Just ten seconds,' cried Milo excitedly. 'Count them off, Tock.'

'Oh, dear, oh dear, oh dear, oh dear,' the bee repeated, continuing to pace nervously.

Then, just as the time ran out, he spelled as fast as he could—'v-e-g-e-t-a-b-l-e-.'

'Correct,' shouted the letter, and everyone cheered.

'Can you spell everything?' asked Milo admiringly.

'Just about,' replied the bee with a hint of pride in his voice. 'You see, years ago I was just an ordinary bee minding my own business, smelling flowers all day, and occasionally picking up part-time work in people's bonnets. Then one day I realized that I'd never amount to anything, without an education and, being naturally adept at spelling, I decided that—'

'BALDERDASH!' shouted a booming voice. And from behind the wagon stepped a large beetle-like insect dressed in a lavish coat, striped trousers, checked waistcoat, spats and a derby hat. 'Let me repeat—BALDERDASH!' he shouted again, swinging his cane and clicking his heels in mid-air. 'Come now, don't be ill-mannered. Isn't someone going to introduce me to the little boy?'

'This,' said the bee with complete disdain, 'is the Humbug. A very dislikable fellow.'

'NONSENSE! Everyone loves a Humbug,' shouted the Humbug. 'As I was saying to the king just the other day—'

'You've never met the king,' accused the bee angrily. Then, turning to Milo, he said 'Don't believe a thing this old fraud says.'

'BOSH!' replied the Humbug. 'We're an old and noble family, honourable to the core—*Insecticus Humbugium,* if I may use the Latin. Why, we fought in the Crusades with Richard the Lion Heart, crossed the Atlantic with Columbus, blazed trails with the pioneers, and today many members of the family hold prominent government positions throughout the world. History is full of Humbugs.'

'A very pretty speech—s-p-e-e-c-h-,' sneered the bee. 'Now why don't you go away? I was just advising the lad of the importance of proper spelling.'

'BAH!' said the bug, putting an arm around Milo. 'As soon as you learn to spell one word, they ask you to spell another. You can never catch up—so why bother? Take my advice, my boy, and forget about it. As my great-great-great-grandfather George Washington Humbug used to say—'

'You sir,' shouted the bee very excitedly, 'are an impostor—i-m-p-o-s-t-o-r- who can't even spell his own name.'

'A slavish concern for the composition of words is the sign of a bankrupt intellect,' roared the Humbug, waving his cane furiously.

Milo didn't have an idea what this meant, but it seemed to infuriate the Spelling Bee, who flew down and knocked off the Humbug's hat with his wing.

'Be careful,' shouted Milo as the bug swung his cane again, catching the bee on the foot and knocking over the box of W's.

'My foot!' shouted the bee.

'My hat!' shouted the bug—and the fight was on.

The Spelling Bee buzzed dangerously in and out of range of the Humbug's wildly swinging cane as they menaced and threatened each other, and the crowd stepped back out of danger.

'There must be some other way to—' began Milo. And then he yelled, 'WATCH OUT,' but it was too late.

There was a tremendous crash as the Humbug in his great fury tripped into one of the stalls, knocking it into another, then another, then another, then another, until every stall in the market place had been upset and the words lay scrambled in great confusion all over the square.

The bee, who had tangled himself in some bunting, toppled to the ground, knocking Milo over on top of him, and lay there shouting, 'Help! Help! There's a little boy on me.' The bug sprawled untidily on a mound of squashed letters and Tock, his alarm ringing persistently, was buried under a pile of words.

Creatures

The animals we capture with words often turn out to be more like us than like themselves. Take Paul Biegel's 'The Wolf's Story', for example, which comes from his marvellous collection of tales 'The King of the Copper Mountains'. Is the Woe-Wolf like a *real* wolf? No more than the Echo-Witch is like a real witch, or the jackal and tiger in Ikram Chugtai's story from Pakistan are like a real jackal and tiger. Animals behaving like human beings are a lot funnier than human beings behaving like animals.

Frederick Brown's 'The Bear' is very different. Here we have a rolling, shaggy poem about a rolling, shaggy creature seen in close-up—and I'd rather be close up to the poem than the creature, wouldn't you? Naomi Lewis's 'A Footprint on the Air' is even more different. While I'm reading it I seem to know exactly what it's about . . . but afterwards I'm not so sure. The mark it makes on me is as mysterious as the bird's own track. Does it have the same effect on you?

This section finishes with Aesop's marvellous fable 'The Traveller and his Dog', which shows how differently a pet and its owner can see things!

The Wolf's Story

PAUL BIEGEL

Long ago, away up in the dark pinewoods of the north, there was a clearing which nobody ever dared enter. The trees stood in a circle round a great heap of stones, jagged like a witch's teeth. And indeed a witch lived in that very spot, or so thought all the wolves. Only the Woe-Wolf thought otherwise.

'There are no such things as witches!' he said. 'And one day, if I ever have time, I'll go to that place and howl at the top of my voice and then you'll see for yourselves she won't appear!'

While he was speaking, the wolves beside him thought they heard the sound of distant laughter, though that, of course, might have been imagination.

The Woe-Wolf glared at them with fierce eyes. 'Don't just stand there trembling!' he cried. 'Come on, let's hunt for something good to eat!'

So off they went, following him two by two until they came to open country where they could run ten abreast.

A little later when the sun went down and

dusk began to fall, they met a huge buffalo that had strayed from the herd. This creature was nearly three times the size of the Woe-Wolf, but without a moment's hesitation and as though his legs were steel springs, he leapt on to its neck.

Then followed a terrible fight in which the Woe-Wolf was jerked to and fro so violently that heaven and earth seemed to him to mix together like porridge. But he never let go for an instant and in the end the buffalo fell dead.

It was a great victory and would certainly have led to quite a celebration had not a strange thing occurred. Suddenly there was a savage snorting behind them and when the Woe-Wolf looked round he saw a still bigger, white buffalo. It immediately wheeled about and set off in the direction of the forest.

'*Woe, woe,* wolves!' cried the Woe-Wolf. 'After him! He's the one for us!'

He at once started after the pale form that galloped through the darkness. Soon he was among the trees, but though their trunks bruised his bones and the brambles tore his coat, he never lost sight of his prey.

'*Woe, woe!*' he cried again, but the ghostly white of the buffalo became fainter and fainter and finally disappeared.

The wolf came to a halt and pricked up his

ears. There was no longer any sound of trampling hoofs, no snorting, no cracking of branches. Was the buffalo hiding?

Stealthily the wolf crept forward, nose to ground, and so came to the clearing where the dark pines stood in a circle round the heap of weird stones.

'Aha, that's where he'll be!' the Woe-Wolf thought and quickly leapt on top of the heap. But the stones parted, or so it seemed to him, and no buffalo was to be seen, nothing but more stones, which now completely surrounded him.

'*Woe, woe!*' the wolf howled.

'*Woe-oe-oe-oe!*' sounded from seven sides as though seven wolves were answering.

'I'm here!' he cried, thinking the wolves had followed him.

But from seven sides came the answer—'*Here-ere-ere-ere!*'

The Woe-Wolf looked about him. Nothing but stones, upright, threatening pieces of rock. No white buffalo. No other wolves.

He was about to move away when he heard a sudden snorting behind him. He whipped round and leapt on to a stone, but beyond it lay only more stones. There was a sound of soft laughter.

'Who's there?' he growled. But seven times the answer rumbled: '*There-ere-ere-ere!*'

The wolf's hackles rose. 'Where are you?' he snarled.

'*Are you-are-you-are-you!*' the answer came. But through it he distinctly heard a voice call: 'Here!'

And with that began a terrible chase after an invisible prey among the echoing stones.

The Woe-Wolf's claws split on the hard rock, his tail lashed against the sharpd edges, and his ears were torn on the jagged points as he ran like a mad thing from stone to stone, for each time the voice called: 'Here I am!' it came from a different direction. To add to his confusion his own howling, '*woe!*' echoed so persistently, that in the end he was forced to stuff his paws into his ears to shut out the noise. Then he lay down panting, dazed and giddy from his mad circling.

It was at this very moment that Here-I-Am appeared. It wasn't a white buffalo. It was the witch.

'Well, wolfy!' she cackled. 'Now you can see for yourself that I *do* exist!' She laughed grimly and the sound rumbled among the stones.

The Woe-Wolf half closed his eyes and with two green slits stared at the witch. 'Who are you?' he asked.

'I am the Echo Witch,' she said. 'And I'm going to change you into a stone, for stone wolves echo very nicely.'

At that the Woe-Wolf laughed. 'I'd like to
see you try!' he said contemptuously. 'If you
dare so much as touch me I'll tear you to
pieces.'

The Echo Witch shook her head, which
made her cheeks flap unpleasantly. 'I needn't
touch you at all,' she said. 'I have only to say
one word of the spell and you'll become a
stone. So just go and sit down quietly.'

The Woe-Wolf got up slowly. Huge and

strong though he was, it would be of little use to spring upon the witch. She had only to step aside and say the magic word and he would drop like a stone to the ground. He had to think of a better plan.

'No,' he said, 'I won't sit, I'll stand as though I were about to spring, then I'll become a much more interesting stone. But you must count up to three before you say the spell.'

'Very well,' said the witch.

It took the Woe-Wolf quite a time to find the right spot. At length he placed himself in front of a big rock, tensed his muscles, nodded to the witch, and waited.

'One, two, three!' cried the witch and uttered the magic word.

But before it was quite out of her mouth the Woe-Wolf, in the biggest leap of his life, sprang and disappeared behind the rock. The spell the witch hurled at him came too late. It bounced against the rock and back onto the witch herself who, with a scream, was instantly turned to stone.

As the Woe-Wolf ran off he passed very close to the witch, and she, with her stone nails, tore a great piece out of his fur. That fur never grew again, neither did the Woe-Wolf of the Bare Flank ever go back to that place.

Some say the witch's last scream still echoes among the stones, but others are sure it is only the wind.

A Footprint On The Air

NAOMI LEWIS

'Stay!' said the child. The bird said, 'No,
My wing has mended, I must go.
I shall come back to see you though,
One night, one day—'
                          'How shall I know?'
'Look for my footprint in the snow.'

'The snow soon goes—oh, that's not fair!'
'Don't grieve. Don't grieve. I shall be there
In the bright season of the year,
One night, one day—'
                          'But tell me, where,'
'Look for my footprint on the air.'

The Farmer's Wife And The Tiger

A story from Pakistan

IKRAM CHUGTAI

One day a farmer went with his bullocks to plough his field. He had just turned the first furrow when a tiger walked up and said, 'Peace be with you, friend. How are you this fine morning?'

'The same to you, my lord, and I am pretty well, thank you,' replied the farmer, quaking with fear but thinking it wisest to be polite.

'I am glad to hear it, because Providence has sent me to eat your two bullocks,' said the tiger cheerfully. 'You are a God-fearing man, I know, so make haste and unyoke them.'

'Aren't you making a mistake, my friend?' asked the farmer. His courage had returned now that he knew the tiger was only proposing to gobble up his bullocks, not him. 'Providence sent me to plough this field and in order to plough, I must have oxen. Hadn't you better go and make further enquiries?'

'There is no need to delay, and I should be sorry to keep you waiting about,' said the tiger.

'If you'll unyoke the bullocks, I'll be ready in a moment to eat them.' With that the tiger began to sharpen his teeth and claws in a very frightening manner.

The farmer begged and prayed that his oxen might not be eaten and promised that, if the tiger would spare them, he would give him in exchange a fine fat young milch-cow of his wife's.

To this the tiger agreed, and taking the oxen with him for safety, the farmer hurried home. Seeing him return so early from the fields, his wife, who was an energetic hard-working woman, called out, 'What! Lazy bones! Back already and my work just beginning!'

The farmer explained how he had met the tiger and that, to save the bullocks, he had promised the milch-cow in exchange. At that his wife began to shout, saying, 'A likely story indeed! What do you mean by saving your stupid old bullocks at the expense of my beautiful cow. Where will the children get milk? How can I cook without butter?'

'All very fine, wife,' retorted the farmer, 'but how can we make bread without corn? How can we have corn without bullocks to plough the fields? It's surely better to do without milk and butter than without bread, so make haste and untie the cow.'

'You great silly!' scolded his wife. 'If you

had an ounce of sense in your brain, you'd think of some plan to get us out of this difficulty.'

'Think of one yourself!' cried her husband in rage.

'So I will,' replied his wife, 'but if I do the thinking, you must do as I say. Go back to the tiger and tell him that the cow wouldn't come with you, but that your wife is bringing it.'

The farmer, who was a great coward, didn't like the idea of going back empty-handed to the tiger, but as he could not think of any other plan, he did as he was told. He found the tiger still sharpening his claws and teeth, he was so hungry. When he heard that he had to wait still longer for his dinner, he began to growl and lash his tail and curl his whiskers in a most terrible manner, causing the poor farmer's knees to knock together with terror.

Now, when the farmer had left the house, his wife went out to the stable and saddled the pony. Then she put on her husband's best clothes, tied the turban very high so as to make her look as tall as possible, jumped astride the pony and set off to the field where the tiger was.

She rode along, swaggering like a man, till she came to where the lane turned into the field, and then she called out as bold as brass,

'Now, please the powers, I may find a tiger in the field! I haven't tasted tiger since yesterday when I ate three for breakfast.'

Hearing these words and seeing the speaker ride boldly towards him, the tiger was so alarmed that he turned tail and bolted into the forest. He went at such a headlong pace that he nearly knocked down his jackal—tigers always have a jackal of their own to clear away the bones after they have finished eating.

'My lord! My lord!' cried the jackal. 'Where are you going so fast?'

'Run! Run!' panted the tiger. 'There's the very devil of a horseman in yonder field who thinks nothing of eating three tigers for breakfast.'

At this the jackal laughed. 'My dear master,' he said, 'the sun has dazzled your eyes. That was no horseman, but only the farmer's wife dressed up as a man!'

'Are you quite sure?' asked the tiger, pausing in his flight.

'Quite sure, my lord,' said the jackal, 'and if your lordship's eyes had not been dazzled—ahem—by the sun, your lordship would have seen the woman's pigtail hanging down behind her.'

'But you may be mistaken,' persisted the cowardly tiger, 'she was the very devil of a horseman to look at!'

'Who's afraid?' replied the jackal. 'Come! Don't give up your dinner because of a woman! We'll go together, if you like.'

'No, you might take me there and then run away and leave me!' said the tiger fearfully.

'Well, let us tie our tails together then, so that I can't!' suggested the cunning jackal. He was determined not to be done out of his bones at the end of the feast.

To this the tiger agreed, and having tied their tails together in a reef-knot, the pair set off arm-in-arm.

Now the farmer and his wife had remained in the field, laughing over the trick they had played on the tiger. Suddenly, lo and behold, what should they see but the tiger and the jackal coming towards them with their tails tied together.

'Run!' cried the farmer. 'We are lost!'

'Nothing of the kind, you great baby,' answered his wife coolly. 'Stop that noise! I can't hear myself speak!'

She waited until the animals were within hail, then called out politely. 'How very kind of you, dear Mr Jackal, to bring me such a nice fat tiger! I shan't be a moment finishing off my share of him and then you can have the bones.'

At these words the tiger became wild with fright, and, quite forgetting the jackal and that reef-knot in their tails, he bolted away full tilt, dragging the jackal behind him. Bumpety, bump, bump, over the stones. Scritch, scratch, scramble, through the briars!

In vain the poor jackal howled and shrieked to the tiger to stop—the noise behind him only frightened the coward more. Away he went, helter-skelter, hurry-scurry, over hill and dale, till he was nearly dead with fatigue, and the jackal was *quite* dead from bumps and bruises.

And the farmer and his wife were never troubled by the tiger again.

The Bear

FREDERICK BROWN

His sullen shaggy-rimmed eyes followed my
    every move,
Slowly gyrating they seemed to mimic the
    movements of his massive head.
Similarly his body rolled unceasingly
From within.
As though each part possessed its own motion
And could think
And move for itself alone.
He had come forward in a lumbering, heavy
    spurt;
Like a beer barrel rolling down a plank.
The tremendous volume of his blood-red
    mouth
Yawned
So casually
But with so much menace.
And still the eye held yours.
So that you had to stay.
And then it turned.
Away.
So slowly.
Back

74

With that same motion
Back
To the bun-strewn
And honey-smelling back of its cage.

The Traveller and his Dog

AESOP

A traveller was about to start on a journey, and said to his Dog, who was stretching himself by the door, 'Come, what are you yawning for? Hurry up and get ready: I mean you to go with me.' But the Dog merely wagged his tail and said quietly, 'I'm ready, master: it's you I'm waiting for.'

Places

I love *places*, especially places where you feel just being there is an adventure. That's why I've chosen Michael Rosen's poem 'In the Playground'. It shows how well-meaning grown-ups can take all the fun out of young people's lives by trying much too hard to look after them. Often it's the very same grown-ups who brag about how daring *they* were as children—the kind of children who'd relish exploring Robert Leeson's 'The Co'vit'. The setting here is so well described I feel it's somewhere I've actually visited. Jamila Gavin's 'China Town' is just as vivid and because it's a real-life place, you can check for yourself whether her story 'John and the Green Dragon' gets it right. Does Agnes Maxwell-Hall's 'Jamaica Market' fit the facts, I wonder? I'd love to find out. Who could resist such a glorious, open-air Harvest Festival?

In The Playground

MICHAEL ROSEN

In the playground
at the back of our house
there have been some changes.

They said the climbing frame was
NOT SAFE
so they sawed it down.

They said the paddling pool was
NOT SAFE
so they drained it dry.

They said the see-saw was
NOT SAFE
so they took it away.

They said the sandpit was
NOT SAFE
so they fenced it in.

They said the playground was
NOT SAFE
so they locked it up.

Sawn down
drained dry
taken away
fenced up
locked up

How do you feel?
Safe?

The Co'vit

ROBERT LEESON

I was in my last year at our school when I had a row with my mates.

We fell out one Saturday over where we wanted to go. I wanted to go to Millbury Woods. Harold and Jammy wanted to go to the Hall.

'You can't get up to the Hall, any road,' I said grumpily. 'The gamekeepers'll stop you. Tommy Mills got shot up there.'

'That's what he says. He a rotten ligger,' said Harold.

'Hey,' said Jammy. 'Come on. It's smashing up at the Hall once you get in over the wall.'

'Yeah, I know,' I jeered, 'miles and miles of wet rhodondendrons.' But I spoiled the sneer because I couldn't say the word let alone spell it.

'Nah,' Jimmy grinned. 'I heard Dad say there's a lot of statues there, women with nothing on and that. You don't find that in Millbury Woods.'

'There's better,' I said.

'Well, what?'

'Well, lots. There's the bridge, and the stream and boat racing.'

'Ah, that's ancient . . .'

I wanted to say—there's the co'vit. But I couldn't make myself utter the word. If I told the real truth I really didn't want them with me. Yet at the same time, I was a bit scared of being on my own.

So when Harold and Jammy said they wouldn't go to the woods, I was half pleased and half annoyed. I looked at Bella hoping she'd decide to come with me. But she didn't. She didn't even say:

'Aw, come on with us.'

In which case I might have changed my mind.

But she said nothing.

'All right,' said Harold, ' be on your own, you misery,' and they turned their backs and walked off up the road.

So in the end I set off for the woods in a bad mood. I was annoyed with them. And I was a bit annoyed with myself. The weather was hot and close. There hadn't been any rain for a fortnight and the fields were yellowing in the sun. The turf on top of Rabbit Hollow was brown, and heat haze was rising on the skyline. My wellies were tight on my feet and the sweat ran down my neck. By the time I got into the woods I had a headache and I was parched. I lay down on the bank above the bridge and had a drink from the stream. It tasted bitter and strange.

Under the trees the air was still and stuffy. Every move in the grass and bushes brought up a cloud of insects that settled on my face. Time and again as I trudged on upstream I wiped them off or flapped my hands to get rid of midges and gnats which hung in clouds over the water. The going became rougher as the ground sloped upwards. I noticed too that the woods were darker than usual. The sky, when I caught a glimpse of it through the trees, was a strange, darkish, steely colour, as though a big lid had been pulled across, and the woods, with me inside, were shut under it. There was no sound, no birds, no small animals rushing off in the bushes.

It was strange. It was as if the woods and the sky were waiting for something and I began to turn round to see if I were really alone.

Now I was in the high part of the woods, scrambling on the slippery overhang with the stream in its narrow bed beneath. The light grew dimmer, the great bank of the canal loomed up in front and the sky overhead had changed from steel grey to steel blue. The sun had vanished. I stopped to get my breath, hooking my arm over an overhanging branch. The culvert I knew was just ahead beyond a fold in the ground.

With a deep breath and a count of twenty I
let go of my branch and half ran, half slipped
over the rise in front of me and came right up
against the huge wall of earth and grass that
towered up above, holding the canal. Twenty
yards to my right was the culvert, a black oval
in the green. I sat down and slithered sideways
over the sloping turf until I could steady myself
on the moss-covered brick arch of the tunnel
entrance.

A breath of damp, stagnant air came up and
I shivered. Below me the stream coursed out
of the ground, its waters foaming and gurgling
over the brickwork. I could not tell how deep
it was here. There was nothing for it but to go
down. Digging my fingers into the brickwork
set in the bank I lowered myself carefully down
the six-foot drop to the bottom curve of the
tunnel. Just as I tried to shift my hold to a
crack in the lower brickwork, my foot slipped.
Down I went, jarring shoulders and hip, land-
ing on all fours in the water. I felt it flood into
my wellies as I grabbed for the tunnel edge and
hauled myself on to the brick curve above
water level. The sides were green with slime
and hard to hold on to. Three times I slid back
before I got a proper grip and stood, clinging
to the inner wall.

Ahead of me the tunnel stretched dark and
cold, but at the end was a faint oval of light,

like the far mouth of the canal at Tunnel Top.

But this was larger and nearer. I reckoned it was fifty yards to the other side. I put a foot out along the brickwork, slipped and found myself sliding into the water again, but clutched in time at a split in the brickwork. My hands were coated with slime now, but I held on. I had no choice. I could not move forward without slipping. Nor could I move back without letting go. Behind, the woods were in thick gloom; ahead, the tunnel even darker.

As I hung there, the sky over the bank split in a silver vein of forked lightning and a massive thunder clap shook the bank. I thought my ear drums would meet in the middle of my head. Without thinking I clapped hands to my ears, let go of the brickwork and went sliding down the greasy circle of the wall into the water. At the last moment I saved myself by throwing my body across the channel so that my hands struck flat against the opposite wall. I was clear of the water but stretched out across it like a mad diver, not falling down but not able to get upright again.

Outside, more lightning. The thunder rang down the tunnel till I thought the whole bank, canal and all, would give way and bury me. I remembered all Ollie had said about the land caving in and my inside went cold. I tried to push up with my hands but the strength was gone from my arms. Yet I couldn't stay there. I knew that. I told myself, saying it out loud. But I could not push upright. Arms and legs were numb with strain, stomach chilled with fright.

The rain was flooding down outside now and as I looked at the stream rushing down the channel below me, I noticed something that made my heart give a jump. The water was turning brown. I knew right away what that meant. The water beyond the canal was rising, the mud stirred up in the stream bed. Before long it would come through the narrow hole in a torrent.

The thought gave me strength. I jerked both hands from the wall and tried to come upright again. But fell back. This time, though, my hands had shifted a foot along the brickwork. To keep my body straight, I edged my feet sideways, farther into the tunnel.

It struck me right away. This was the way to go. Sideways. I jerked up my hands again and half-fell to the right, breaking my fall again, hands on wall. Then I shifted my feet again and again. I was moving like a crab about a yard a minute, but I was moving. Forgetting the thunder, the lightning, the flood water, my fears, everything. I set my mind on getting through that tunnel. At the end of the culvert the white circle grew lighter and lighter. I made out the stream on the other side, high green banks and overhanging willow trees. Beyond that a slope with more trees. I speeded up, slipping and sliding now and then, but more sure of my feet and hands, until with three last sideways heaves I was on a ledge at the lip of the tunnel on the other side. I was through and at the edge of the little green valley with the stream now foaming with flood water in front of me.

Overhead the thunder died away, the rain stopped and above the trees the dark sky opened into blue, grey and white streaks. As I jumped from the ledge to the bank of the stream to clamber to the top, the sun came through, suddenly warm on the back of my neck. At the top of the valley I paused and looked back. Behind me the great canal embankment and the tree tops beyond. But ahead!

I stood and stared. From my vantage point I could see a whole new world, great patches of water glinting in the sun, islands with purple flowering bushes, huge weed-covered cinder heaps, ravines filled with shrubs, a winding track and broken white bridge, and beyond, roofs and walls half sunk into the water. I felt like every explorer since time began. With a yell I rushed down the track towards the bridge. Half way there I stopped and turned aside to peer down into a gully, full from top to bottom with blackberry bushes, a mass of blossom. Wait till I told our Mam. We'd pick tons of berries here in August and September.

Running on I caught with the corner of my eye the shine of sun on glass. To my left was a ruined house, like a farm.

Leading up to it was a splendid row of white-and-pink-blossomed horse chestnut trees. There'd be millions of conkers in a few months' time.

I followed the track where it ran, banked up with ash and cinders between the flashes. Now it wound up to a ridge and as I mounted this I saw I was only on the edge of my discovery. Before me was a great stretch of bush-studded moor, with larger lakes, clumps of small trees and like an ancient city, the ruins of old workings, a network of grass and moss-covered walls forming caverns and arches, trenches and dugouts. I dodged madly among the ruins, peering here, poking there, noting in my mind places to explore when I had more time.

Beyond the workings, more open space with more blackberry bushes than I'd ever seen in my life. Farther off still, more flashes glinting in the hot sun. At first I did not grasp it, but these flashes did not reflect the sky. They had their own colour, a weird emerald green and whitey blue. It was not water, but a great

expanse of chemical waste stretching in front of me, dead like some landscape on the Moon. I pulled brick from a broken wall and hurled it into the nearest pool. It rested a second on the green crust and then sank slowly into the ooze.

I looked round me now, for I'd been running and charging round for about an hour. The woods and canal were well behind me. I was alone in my own fantastic world. But where was I?

Then I saw on the skyline, the unmistakable great grey-brown plume of smoke that marked the Works. I headed towards it and beyond the last green-blue lake, came to a final ridge and looked down into the valley, at the curve of the river and farther along the wooded hill that marked home. Half an hour later I'd reached the canal a mile or so from Tarcroft and was trotting along the tow path. I ran easily as if my excitement had given me a second wind. The damp in my clothes had dried in the sun. As I ran, the Works buzzer sounded across the river.

I stopped, alarmed. Was that the twelve o'clock or the one o'clock?

Down the slope I saw the men on foot and on bike, stream over the bridge. They were heading away from the Works. It was twelve o'clock. It was amazing. All the things I'd done and I'd only been away three hours and I could get home easily for dinner. It was just right, smashing, a bonzer day and all on my own.

After dinner I rushed out in the street. I wasn't going to call for Jammy or Harold or Bella, oh no. But if they happened to be around . . . I might just tell them a bit of what they'd missed. But there was no sign of them. They must have gone off somewhere. I felt flat after the morning's excitement.

I trailed off along the Lane, half hoping they might be there, but the Lane was empty. I wandered round corners and side turnings until I heard shouting in the distance. There was a football game on the rec. Might as well go and watch. I wasn't a real game, just a crowd of kids booting a ball between the goal posts, charging about in a big crowd, changing position. Even the goalie was up with the rest, trying to score.

The ball shot out of the scrimmage and landed near my feet. I belted it back and a lad trapped it with his foot. He grinned and waved. It was Tosher.

'Hey up. Come on. You can be on our side.'

I didn't waste any more time but rushed in kicking with the rest. 'Haven't seen you down here in donkey's years,' said Tosher.

'Been doing things. Hey up, Tosher, there's a smashing place down the canal. . . .'

John And The Green Dragon

JAMILA GAVIN

John lay in bed asleep. He was dreaming of cars, motorbikes and flying into danger with Batman.

Downstairs his mother, father and two big brothers were busy in the family restaurant. The Hong Kong Chinese Restaurant stood in a row of shops in the high street of a small, country town. The neon light flashed on and off all day and night—'TAKE AWAY . . . TAKE AWAY . . .'. People did indeed come to take away a delicious, hot bag of Chinese food and rush home to eat it in front of the television. Other people liked to have a meal out just for a treat, and they could come into the restaurant and sit under the red-tasselled lanterns, leaning over the menu with watering mouths.

It was the night of the Chinese New Year. The swing doors flapped to and fro as steaming dishes were carried through to hungry people. Chicken with sliced almonds, green peppers and special fried rice at Table 26; shark fin soup followed by crispy duck and bamboo shoots at Table 11; spare ribs in black bean sauce, sweet and sour pork, bird's nest soup and beef chop suey all at Table 5 . . . the smells wafted upstairs, but John did not stir. Not so long ago he had had his favourite supper of egg, sausages, baked beans and chips.

Outside, the moon hung like a great lantern. Suddenly a shadow darkened the moonlit sky. John awoke. He could hear a rustling and whirling—like wind; a crackling and sparkling—like fire; a looping and swooping—like waves.

Outside his window John saw a green head bobbing up and down—a dragon's head—with red, glowing eyes and a long, flaming tongue darting in and out between huge, spiky, white teeth. The dragon squeezed himself between the open windows. His jagged, green body and long, long tail came trailing inside and coiled itself around the room like a giant kite.

'Hello,' said John politely. 'Can I help you?'

'I've flown all the way from China,' said the Green Dragon. 'Over snowy mountains and icy lakes; winding rivers and smoking factories; over vast fields of rice and wheat—and now I am so hungry I could swallow up your mother's kitchen.'

'Oh please don't do that,' cried John. 'My mother and father are very proud of their kitchen. They say that we cook the best Chinese food outside London. I help too with sorting out the knives, forks and spoons and our customers call me Hong Kong John.'

'Well then, Hong Kong John,' said the Green Dragon, 'since I am so hungry, and since it is the Chinese New Year, I think I should savour some of your famous food. After all—I am an expert. I have eaten at the finest tables in China—at feasts given by the great emperors themselves!'

'You must be very old if you have eaten with the emperors of China,' said John.

'Several hundred—maybe even a thousand,' boasted the dragon. 'Now then—about this food—I would like to eat deep fried pork with delectable seaweed; braised beef with soya sauce and noodles; bean curd with crab meat; king fried prawns with heavenly vegetables of the four seasons; but to start with I must sharpen my teeth on succulent spare ribs, and I'll finish with a bowl of lychees to sweeten me up. All this must be accompanied with a constant flow of hot, sweet-scented Jasmine tea—pots and pots of it. Well? What are you waiting for?' The Green Dragon looked at John impatiently.

'I . . . I can't get all *that*!' gasped John.

'Can't you?' The Dragon looked downcast. He whisked his tail and ground his teeth. 'Well, what can you get me then?'he asked sulkily.

'I might be able to get you something from the set menus,' said John. 'You know—select a dish from A, B, C or D—and you get three courses all for 80p.'

The Green Dragon heaved and rumbled. 'I don't care what you get me, anything, but get it fast before I start nibbling your curtains. I am absolutely starving!'

John crept downstairs. He peered through the bamboo screens at the bustling restaurant. His brothers looked like jugglers as they balanced plates and dishes piled high as pagodas, hurrying with orders from table to table. His father was mixing drinks at the bar, while his mother bent over sizzling saucepans in the kitchen behind. John tip-toed to the corner of the kitchen where they prepared the set menus. Taking one or two silver foil boxes he quickly

92

scooped in some fried rice, chicken chop suey, a pancake roll, a few crispy balls of sweet and sour pork and a pineapple fritter. The dragon sucked everything into his mouth—boxes and all! 'Where is the tea . . . the tea. . . I must have some tea—I did tell you . . .'

'I really could not manage the tea,' said John hoping that the dragon was not going to make trouble. 'I can get lemonade.' After gulping down several bottles of lemonade, the dragon licked his lips, stretched till it seemed he would push through the ceiling, then pointed his head towards the window. 'Are you ready to go?'

'Ready to go,' asked John, puzzled. 'Go where?'

'Why, to London of course,' said the dragon. 'I've come thousands of miles to see the New Year celebrations in . . . what is the name of that place . . . So . . . Ho . . .?'

'Soho!' cried John—'but that's a hundred miles from here.'

'I came from China in only a moment or two, we'll be in London in a jiffy,' boasted the dragon. Filled with excitement, John clambered on to the dragon's back and snuggled between his great wings with his arms clasped around his neck. 'Which way?' asked the dragon as they rose high into the sky.

'We always go up the motorway,' replied John.

The motorway shone below them in the moonlight like a winding silver ribbon. The cars and lorries flitted to and fro like dazzling insects. The next moment London lay below them—a million scattered lights. They swooped down over the river Thames and followed it up to Westminster. They turned left at Big Ben, up Pall Mall, past the Horse Guards, over Trafalgar Square and on up to Piccadilly. Suddenly a rocket sped up into the air showering them with sparks. 'I think we've arrived,' said the Green Dragon.

John could see a flutter of red flags and fairy lights garlanded across the street from roof-top to roof-top. Clashing cymbals and rattling drums filled the air. Laughing people danced about wearing strange masks, carrying streamers and gaily painted lanterns. A great paper lion wheeled in and out of the crowd, roaring and leaping as children chased and teased it.

'They must have known I was coming!' yelled the dragon. 'Look! They've hung the cabbages from their windows for me—I love cabbages.'

From almost every window, John could see Chinese cabbages dangling from the ends of string. For a moment the noise and frenzy of the crowd hushed in amazement as the Green Dragon came rushing in among them. Then there was a cheer of joy and everyone burst out laughing and shouting as the dragon zig-zagged from window to window gobbling up the cabbages. Children followed, pressing red-dyed melon seeds into John's hands and tossing red envelopes up to him with gifts inside. All around fireworks sprayed the sky and fire-crackers spluttered at their feet.

'It's years since I saw a dragon dance,' murmured an elderly Chinese shopkeeper.

As the dance grew wilder, John's arms began to ache. He felt as if he were on a merry-go-round which would not stop. At last he could hold on no longer; his tired fingers loosened and he began to slide off the dragon's back. The dragon rollicked on through the crowd. John slithered to the ground, and before he could look around he was swept away by merry-makers and dancers. He tried to struggle after the Green Dragon, but gradually he found himself carried out of sight—down side streets and up narrow alleys. Just as he was beginning to feel very lost, he felt a hand in his and turned to find a little girl at his side.

'You are the dragon boy, aren't you?' she said.

'Yes, but I've lost him,' said John sadly, 'and I can't get home without him.'

'Oh don't worry,' replied the girl, 'he'll find you when it's time. What is your name?'

'John,' said John, 'but some people call me

Hong Kong John. My Chinese name is Ying-Chai.'

'Ying-Chai!' the girl exclaimed. 'I like that for it means "Very Brave" and you must be brave to ride on a dragon's back. My name is Hoi-Au which means "Seagull". My English name is Marina.'

The children gaily jostled along the streets, chewing on melon seeds and dodging the firecrackers.

'I feel as if I were in China,' shouted John.

'Well, people do call this place "China Town" as there are many Chinese families living round here. Come and visit my house, we are nearly there.' They stopped outside a curio shop filled with Chinese statuettes of jade and marble; paintings and ornaments; precious silks and manuscripts.

'This is my father's shop,' said Marina. 'We live upstairs above the shop.'

John followed Marina upstairs and entered a room full of friendly people. They all turned with smiling faces and out-stretched hands of welcome to greet them. Marina's mother came forward. 'Hello, dragon boy, I am delighted to have you in my home.' She bowed, then put a hand on his shoulder and gently sat him down as she could see that he was tired.

'His name is Ying-Chai,' Marina told them. Then everyone gathered round him and offered him Chinese sweets—salted, dried apricots, sweet and sour bananas; and there were bowls of prawn crackers and hot tea or lemonade.

John met the rest of Marina's family. 'These are my two brothers and sister. We are all at school in the neighbourhood. This is my most respected eldest uncle, Mr Tsin. He owns a restaurant just round the corner. My most honoured grandfather is Mr Leung and he owns a bookshop two streets away.' John bowed deeply to Mr Tsin and Mr Leung and they bowed back to him.

'My family have a restaurant miles out of London in the country,' John contributed.

Everyone smiled. The night passed. A sudden swell of sound from the crowd sent everyone running to the window. John saw the Green Dragon being carried along by cheering merry-makers. As they drew near, the dragon called up to the window where John was leaning out anxiously, 'It's time to go home now, John!'

John turned to Marina and her family and wished them goodbye. 'Thank you for looking after me,' he said, 'and I hope you will visit me in the country, one day.'

The dragon hovered outside the windows and John climbed out on to his back.

'Goodbye John! Goodbye, Ying-Chai, brave dragon boy!' called his friends.

As the dragon turned westwards, the first glow of dawn was beginning to light up the horizon behind them. The last rocket spluttered to the ground, and the lanterns already looked dimmer by the new light of day. John saw no more. The dragon flew back down the motorway with the boy fast asleep between his wings. A few early morning workers, who happened to glance up at the sky, were amazed to see such a high-flying kite with its long, long tail among the pink-streaked clouds.

The next morning John awoke to find his mother by his bed. 'Happy New Year, John,' she beamed. 'Welcome to the Year of the Dragon. Here is a parcel which has come all the way from your uncle in China.'

John carefully unwrapped the paper and uncovered a large, flat box. Hardly daring to breathe he lifted the lid. There lay a huge, green, paper kite shaped like a dragon, with red, glowing eyes, a long, flaming tongue between spiky, white teeth.

'I've flown all the way from China . . .' the dragon seemed to be saying, '. . . over snowy mountains and icy lakes; winding rivers and smoking factories . . . vast fields of rice and wheat . . . and . . .'

Jamaica Market

AGNES MAXWELL-HALL

Honey, pepper, leaf-green limes,
Pagan fruit whose names are rhymes,
Mangoes, breadfruit, ginger-roots,
Granadillas, bamboo-shoots,
Cho-cho, ackees, tangerines,
Lemons, purple Congo-beans,
Sugar, okras, kola-nuts,
Citrons, hairy coconuts,
Fish, tobacco, native hats,
Gold bananas, woven mats,
Plantains, wild-thyme, pallid leeks,
Pigeons with their scarlet beaks,
Oranges and saffron yams,
Baskets, ruby guava jams,
Turtles, goat-skins, cinnamon,
Allspice, conch-shells, golden rum.
Black skins, babel—and the sun
That burns all colours into one.

Trees

Does staring at trees send you into a dream? That's what happens to me. Maybe it's why I like the gorgeous moodiness of Robert Frost's poem so much—and why I can understand how upset the little green fairy was in Beatrix Potter's story about the cutting down of an old oak. What is it about trees which stirs up our deepest feelings? Philip Larkin's poem gives one answer.

Tree At My Window

ROBERT FROST

Tree at my window, window tree,
My sash is lowered when night comes on;
But let there never be curtain drawn
Between you and me.

Vague dream-head lifted out of the ground,
And thing next most diffuse to cloud,
Not all your light tongues talking aloud
Could be profound.

But, tree, I have seen you taken and tossed,
And if you have seen me when I slept,
You have seen me when I was taken and swept
And all but lost.

That day she put our heads together,
Fate had her imagination about her,
Your head so much concerned with outer,
Mine with inner, weather.

The Fairy In The Oak

BEATRIX POTTER

The fairy in the oak had been a harmless timid
spirit for many hundred years. Long ago, when
the oak was a sapling, there had been wolves;
and the dalesmen hunted them with hounds.
The hunt swept through the forest; the frightened fairy leaped into the oak branches. She
found the tree a place of refuge; therefore she
loved it and made it her home. Because it had
a guardian fairy, that oak grew tall and strong.
It held up its head against wind and snow; and
scorned the wintry weather.

But the Surveyor of the District Council has
no sentiment; and no respect, either for fairies or
for oaks! He decided to widen the road for motor

cars. So one day there came the surveyor, his assistant with the chain links, two men who carried the theodolite with three legs; a woodmonger; and four members of the Council. They did much measuring with the chains; they made notes in their pocketbooks; they squinted through the theodolite at white and black sticks. Then they clambered up the rocks, and stared at the fairy's oak. The woodmonger measured it with a tape measure; he measured near the foot of the butt; he measured again six foot up; he reckoned the quarter girth; they did calculations according to Hoppus. The councillors said that the tree had an enormous butt; thirty foot run of clean timber to the first branch, with never a knot. They looked at the rocks round about; and did sums. Then they went away.

In January a number of men arrived; they had tools, and wheelbarrows, and carts, and a wooden hut. They were quarrymen, navvies, wood-fellers; and carters and wagoners with horses. They cleared away the underwood; they drilled and blasted the rocks. The noise of blasting was like thunder; it awoke every fairy in the wood.

And they felled the fairy's oak.

For three days they hacked and sawed and drove wedges; the wood was as Hard as iron. Their axes broke; their saws were nipped; they lost their wedges overhead in the cuts. But day after day they laboured, and swung heir heavy axes; and drove iron wedges with sledge hammer blows into the great tree's heart. Then one climbed the tree and tied a wire rope to its head; and they pulled with a wagon horse. The tree swayed and groaned, and the hawser broke. Again they wielded their axes; and the little fairy sobbed and cried with pain.

Suddenly, with a rending shriek and a roar, the oak thundered down amongst the rocks!

It lamed a horse, and it did the men a mischief.

All next day they hacked and sawed; they cut off its head and arms. They left the trunk lying overnight beside the road. The fairy stayed beside it, and caused another accident, upsetting a farmer's cart. His horse in the dusk saw a thing like a little green squirrel that scolded and wrung its hands.

Next day came the wagoners to hoist the great tree; and then again there was disaster. The three legs slipped; the chains broke twice—was it the fury of the little angry spirit that beat against the chains and snapped them?

At length the tree was loaded. They drew away the wagon with two extra pairs of horses; and the fairy, sullen and exhausted, sat huddled upon the log. They swept the top stones off the walls; they had every sort of trouble; but at last they reached the summit of the moor. Ten chain horses were unhooked; leaving one trembling hill-horse in the shafts. The brake was screwed on hard, to face the steep descent.

Down below the hill there sounded a humming, whirring sound—the noise of the sawmill. The fairy sprang from her tree, and fled away into the woods.

All winter she wandered homeless. One day she climbed into one tree; another day she climbed into another tree. She always chose an oak tree; but she could not settle to sleep. When-ever a load of sawn timber came back up the road from the sawmill, the fairy came down to the road.

She looked at it wistfully; but it was always larch, or ash, or plane; not oak.

She wandered further afield in spring time,

into the meadows outside the woods. There was grass for the lambs in the meadows; on the trees young green leaves were budding—but no new green leaves for the oak fairy. Her leaf-gown was tattered and torn.

One day she sat on a tree-top, and the west wind blew over the land. It brought sounds of lambs bleating; and the cuckoo calling. And a strange new sound from the river—clear ring-ing blows upon oak.

'Men do not fell trees in May, when the sap rises. Why does this sound stir my heart, and make my feet dance, in spite of me? Can I hear cruel hammers and saws upon oak-wood, and feel glad?' said the fairy of the oak.

She came out of the wood, and her feet danced across the meadow, through the cuckoo flowers and marsh mary-golds, to the banks of the flooded stream, where men were building a bridge. A new bridge to the farm, where none had been before; a wooden bridge with a broad span across the rushing river; and the straight brave timbers that spanned it were made of the fairy's oak!

The Trees

PHILIP LARKIN

The trees are coming into leaf
Like something almost being said;
The recent buds relax and spread,
Their greenness is a kind of grief.

Is it that they are born again
And we grow old? No, they die too.
Their yearly trick of looking new
Is written down in rings of grain.

Yet still unresting castles thresh
In fullgrown thickness every May.
Last year is dead, they seem to say,
Begin afresh, afresh, afresh.

Outsiders

I never get tired of meeting people—best of all people who are odd in some way, who don't quite fit. This section offers four of them, beginning with Gerda Mayer's Flo. She's the sort of old lady who's still got a twinkle in her eye—or maybe I mean a twinkle in her step. Poor Toothie, in Gene Kemp's story, has lost his sparkiness though. At least, he has until his wild pet Cat arrives in the nick of time. Miss Hubbard isn't so lucky. Peter Dixon who wrote the poem tells me she really existed. So did someone like Mr Wade in my own story. It's a sad fact that people who don't quite fit are often very badly treated by those who fit only too well.

Flo

GERDA MAYER

There is a dotty woman
Who when she does her shopping
And sees a hopscotch in the street
Goes hophop hophop hopping.

A game she often wins
Though no one else is there;
She plays a childhood friend, who'd now
Be quite as old as her.

And sometimes she denounces
That friend of long ago,
And says to all the empty air:
You KNOW you cheated, Flo!

Visiting Mr Wade

CHRIS POWLING

Kit took a deep breath. If he didn't go down the alley soon, Mum would be coming out to look for him—or even worse, she'd send his brother Pete to find out why he was taking so long. 'What are you hanging about for?' Pete would say. 'Scared of Mr Wade, are you?'

And he'd see at once it was true and never let Kit forget it. Being teased by Pete was as bad as visiting Mr Wade. Well, nearly.

Kit thought of the last time he'd been down the alley. It was easy then because Mum was with him. She'd done all the talking in a voice that was gentle and friendly—not at all the way she spoke to him and Pete. 'How are you today, Mr Wade? The shoes are ready, are they? Ah yes, here's the price chalked on the sole. Thank you Mr Wade. You've done a lovely job as usual.'

Was Mum frightened of the shoe mender as well, Kit wondered.

Most people were, after all, because Mr Wade had only half a face. He wore special glasses to hide this, one side normal and the other side bulging with a wobbly, glittery false eye. 'Know what he does with it at night?' Pete whispered. 'He bounces it up and down on the end of a bit of elastic, like a yo-yo!'

'You're horrible!' Kit protested.

Me?' said Pete. 'Mr Wade's eye is, you mean.' And he held up his hand with fingers cupped into an eye-shape pointing this way and that like a periscope.

Which explained why Kit was still dithering at the entrance to the alley where Mr Wade had his shed. You don't have to worry yet, Kit told himself desperately, not even when you're in his back yard. He always stays in the hut, working, doesn't he? So before he could lose his nerve, Kit sprinted along the track between the houses, skidded to a halt at Mr Wade's back gate, lifted the latch, slipped inside and swung the gate shut behind him, all in a moment.

One of his last moments alive, maybe.

For Mr Wade wasn't in his shed at all. He was just across the yard, bending over a cucumber frame. At the click of the latch, he'd gone rigid.

Kit was rigid too. He knew there was no move he could make—even blinking was beyond him. He'd have to go on looking while Mr Wade slowly turned half a face towards him, the false eye jiggling in its socket. Kit would be the first kid in the world to see it in broad daylight.

Except Mr Wade didn't turn round.

Instead he straightened up and took a step to one side, careful to keep his back to Kit. Then came another step, then another—sideways like a crab. When he got to the shed door, he opened it and stepped through still sideways, still making sure there was no chance at all Kit would see a yo-yo eye in half a face.

Kit stared at the shed door. Mr Wade was safe enough now he was back in his shadowy workshop. The problem would come after Kit crossed the yard, went inside and handed over the shoes he'd brought for mending. How could he get his voice to sound as gentle and friendly as Mum's?

Miss Hubbard

PETER DIXON

She's at the window again!
Bug eyed,
Dressing gowned, and grey.
'See her!' squeal the brownie pack
Returning from St Johns.
'See her!' chorus the boys
Returning from nowheremuch.

And there she stares—
Tall
And gaunt
And hair unpinned . . .
Staring
Staring
Staring
Staring beyond the silver slates of Stanley
    Street
Of Wilmer Way
And distant Arnos Grove.

Head tilted,
As if by mechanical device.
Unmoving,
And unflinching of the handful of gravel
Thrown at her window by the captain of the
  Boys' Brigade.
Always staring.
Never watching,
Always staring.
Staring at her moon.

'Miss Hubbbard's moon starin'' bellowed the
  boy
Who always delivered the classified late.
'Miss Hubbard's moon starin'' echoed the
  Bunyan boys
from 43.
And the children gathered,
And the pink fingers pointed,
And the gravel rattled.
And still she stared.

And from the houses the grown ups came—
Nodding
And whispering

And pointing
And murmuring wise things amongst
  themselves
To lead the children away.

Later that year they also led Miss Hubbard
  away,
Slowly
And kindly . . .
For staring at the moon.

Toothie And Cat

GENE KEMP

High on the hills above the city was a cave, well hidden away among the trees and the rocks and the bracken. And in that cave lived an old tramp with a gingery, greyish beard hanging to his waist, a greasy hat on his head, string tied just below the knees of his trousers, and one tooth that stuck out over his beard. Because of this he was known as Toothie, and he couldn't remember any other name. He couldn't remember very much at all, for his brain was as foggy as a November night. He was never bright even in his prime and he hadn't improved with the years. Nobody had ever cared for him much ever since his mother dumped him, wrapped in an old blanket, outside a police station, and then made off as fast as she could. Toothie tried to keep away from police stations ever after.

Below the hills in the city lived Cat. Cat the Black and the Bad, a streak of a cat with claws as sharp as daggers and a heart as black as his tatty fur. No one loved Cat. Once he was dropped in a river and left to drown. But you don't drown animals like Cat that easily. He got out, and survived, by hatred, mostly. He hated people and children and bright lights and kindness. He loved fighting and stealing, roof-tops and alleys, and, most of all, dustbins. He relied on them when the birds grew careful, or too many kitchen doors were shut. In the daytime he thieved and slept on walls in patches of sunlight. At night he rampaged across roof-tops, wailing and caterwauling. So he lived for some years, till one morning he dropped from a roof-top a bit carelessly, and a car speeding through the dawn grazed his leg. Snarling and swearing, he limped to the side of the road, where Toothie, who had also been raiding dustbins, found him. He was pleased, for he'd found a very meaty chicken carcase.

He walked all round Cat, who spat at him. Then he popped a bit of chicken into the complaining mouth, and Cat stopped spitting, and ate instead. Toothie popped him in his old bag, and went back to the cave, where he made some chicken soup and tied a big leaf round the injured leg. After a time Cat stopped spit-ting at him, for he'd grown to like Toothie's smell. His leg healed.

Cat did not return to the city. It was summer. He hunted and Toothie cooked: stews and soups in his iron pot, other tasty dishes baked in mud packed at the base of the fire. Long warm days passed by in the green wood

and the dark cave. Sometimes Toothie would sing and Cat purr, both rusty noises. That autumn was beautiful, warm and golden, with more nuts than had been seen for years. Toothie and Cat were well fed and content.

Until the night the October wind arrived, blowing cold, stripping the leaves off the trees, and it brought with it the sound of cats singing in the city below. Cat stirred in his sleep and woke up. He left Toothie's warmth to sit in the mouth of the cave, listening. Yes, there, again, came the yowling of cats. Cat shivered. He looked once at the old man, asleep, and slipped out into the night.

A fortnight later he came back, hungry,

limping, wet and exhausted, longing for Toothie's warm fire, Toothie's food, Toothie's smelly company. But the cave was empty. The iron pot hung forlornly by the burnt-out fire. Toothie had gone.

Cat sat and washed himself, which is what cats do when they don't know what to do next. Then he searched through the woods, crying his strange, wild call. There was no Toothie. Cat slew an unwary bird who would have done better to have migrated and, still hungry, set off for the city.

Through the streets he ran, sniffing, investigating, fighting, always searching for Toothie's fascinating smell, and one day, a week or so later, he arrived at the City Hospital and knew that his friend was inside.

Now Cat was much cleverer than Toothie, and he knew from the smell of the hospital that that was where people were ill, and his cat brain put illness and chicken together. He'd got to find some chicken.

He tried as many houses as he had paws before he finally crept into a gleaming, shiny bright kitchen, and there on the immaculate tiled surface lay a scrumptious chicken leg on a plate of crisp salad. The salad Cat ignored, he was not a lettuce-eater, but he seized the chicken and was just about to leap through the partially open window when the owner appeared, screamed like a whistling kettle and spent the rest of the day feeling very ill indeed, and telling anyone who could be made to listen how a fiendish monster had appeared like a black demon in her sacred kitchen. Cat kept increasing in size till he reached the dimensions of a mini-tiger.

A while later, the mini-tiger sat outside the hospital door and waited, chicken portion gripped firmly in teeth. Going in at the front door didn't seem like a good idea—it looked too busy and important. Cat had never liked front doors, anyway. Back or side doors were for the likes of him. So he slunk round the corner till he came to a dark staircase that went up and up and on and on. Right at the top were dozens of dustbins. Cat purred through the chicken. He liked those dustbins, homely and friendly, they were.

Beyond them was a door with two little round glass panels. It opened in the middle and swung as someone walked through. And Cat slid in, keeping a very low profile. He ran, chicken in mouth and stomach almost on the floor, through rows of beds, and then into another ward with yet more beds. In the third a little boy lay in bed, bored. He sat up and cried:

'There's a cat. It's got something in its mouth. Good ole puss cat. Come here.'

He wanted Cat a lot, but Cat ran on. But now that he was spotted, pandemonium broke loose.

'Catch that cat!'

'Stop him!'

'Get that filthy animal out of here!'

As fast as he could, Cat ran on. Patients shouted as nurses ran to grab him.

But nothing could stop Cat now. Like a rocket swooshing into space, Cat shot down the ward to find Toothie. He dodged trolleys, ran under beds, ran over beds, squeezed between legs, narrowly missed cleaners, tripped up nurses carrying vases of flowers or trays, scattering people right and left to reach the bed with the screens round it where Toothie lay dying.

He'd collapsed with pneumonia a week after Cat had left him and somehow, shivering, coughing, full of pains, he'd crawled to the road, where a bus driver had driven him straight to the hospital despite complaints from some of the passengers. And since then, Toothie had lain in terror of the bright lights, the uniforms, the smells and the sounds, all too much for his mazed mind. He wanted to die.

Sister's voice rang out loud and clear.

'Stop that beast! It's got germs!'

Hands grabbed at Cat, missing narrowly. He shot through the screens and the doctor and nurses beside Toothie and up on to the bed. There on the whiter than white, brighter than bright, snowy, frosty, bleached, purified, disinfected, sterilised, decontaminated pillow Cat laid the dusty, greasy, tooth-marked chicken leg, just beside Toothie's head.

Shouts were all about him.

But Toothie's eyes opened and he saw Cat. A triumphant burst of purring sounded through the ward. Come what might, Cat had arrived. He'd found Toothie.

Last Word

Well, that's it . . . very nearly. I'm relying on you to help me uncross my fingers by adding your own favourite poems and stories to the ones I've included. Mind you, even then you won't be satisfied that the anthology's complete. No anthology ever can be for the reason suggested by the poem I've saved till last, Russell Hoban's 'The Jigsaw Puzzle'.

Goodbye!

The Jigsaw Puzzle

RUSSELL HOBAN

My beautiful picture of pirates and treasure
Is spoiled, and almost I don't want to start
To put it together; I've lost all the pleasure
I used to find in it: there's one missing part.

I know there's one missing—they lost it, the
others,
The last time they played with my puzzle—
and maybe
There's more than one missing: along with the
brothers
And sisters who borrow my toys there's the
baby.

There's a hole in the ship or the sea that it sails
on,
And I said to my father, 'Well, what shall I
do?'
It isn't the same now that some of it's gone,'
He said, 'Put it together; the world's like that
too.'

Acknowledgements

The author and publishers gratefully acknowledge permission to reprint copyright material to the following:

'The Night Bird' © Ursula Wolfel from *The Light and the Dark*, published by Lutterworth Press (1972). 'The Invisible Beast' © Jack Prelutsky from *The Headless Horseman Rides Tonight*, published by A & C Black (1984). 'Journey's End' © Michael McHugh. 'Jacob Two-Two Meets the Hooded Fang' © Mordecai Richler, from *Jacob Two-Two*, published by André Deutsch (1975). 'Charley's Swear Word' © Sheila Lavelle from *My Best Fiend*, published by Hamish Hamilton (1979). 'The Word Party' © Richard Edwards, from *The Word Party*, published by Lutterworth Press (1986). 'Confusion in the Market Place' text © Norton Juster (1961), an extract from *The Phantom Tollbooth*, published by Collins (Fontana Lions 1974). 'The Wolf's Story' © Paul Biegel, from *The King of the Copper Mountains*, published by JM Dent & Sons Ltd (1969). 'A Footprint on the Air' © Naomi Lewis, from *A Footprint on the Air*, published by Hutchinson Books Ltd (1983). 'The Farmer's Wife and the Tiger' by Ikram Chugtai from *The Magic Umbrella* © Eileen Colwell (ed.), published by The Bodley Head (1976). 'The Bear' by Frederick Brown © Oxford University Press (1964), reprinted from *Every Man Will Shout* (edited by Roger Mansfield & Isobel Armstrong (1964), by permission of OUP. 'In the Playground' © Michael Rosen from *When Did You Last Wash Your Feet*, published by André Deutsch (1986). 'The Co'vit' © Robert Leeson from *Harry & Bella, Jammy & Me*, published by Collins (Fontana Lions). 'John and the Green Dragon' © Jamila Gavin from *The Orange Tree and Other Stories*, published by Methuen Children's Books (1979). 'Jamaica Market ' © Agnes Maxwell-Hall, from *Sugar and Spice* by Guiseppe, published by Macmillan (Caribbean), and reprinted by permission of Macmillan London & Basingstoke. 'Tree at My Window' © The Estate of Robert Frost, from *The Poetry of Robert Frost*, edited by Edward Connery Lathem, published by Jonathan Cape Ltd. 'The Trees' © Philip Larkin from *High Windows*, published by Faber & Faber Ltd. 'Flo' © Gerda Mayer, from *The Knockabout Show*, originally published by Chatto & Windus (1978). 'Toothie and the Cat' © Gene Kemp, from *Dog Days and Cat Naps*, published by Faber & Faber Ltd. 'Miss Hubbard' © Peter Dixon. 'The Jigsaw Puzzle' © Russell Hoban, from *All Sorts of Poems*, reprinted by permission of David Higham Associates Ltd.

The publishers have made every effort to trace copyright holders. If we have inadvertently omitted to acknowledge anyone we should be most grateful if this would be brought to our attention for correction at the first opportunity.

127